GO HANG A SALAMI! I'M A LASAGNA HOG!

GO HANG A SALAMI!

I'M A LASAGNA HOG!

and Other Palindromes by JON AGEE

A TRUMPET CLUB SPECIAL EDITION

To Hannah

ISBN 0-590-99516-2

Copyright © 1991 by Jon Agee.
All rights reserved. Published by Scholastic Inc.,
555 Broadway, New York, NY 10012,
by arrangement with Farrar, Straus, Giroux, Inc.
TRUMPET and the TRUMPET logo are registered
trademarks of Scholastic Inc.

12 11 10 9 8 7 6 5 4 3 2 1   6 7 8 9/9 0 1/0

Printed in the U.S.A.

TAHITI HAT

SALT AN
ATLAS

SMART RAMS

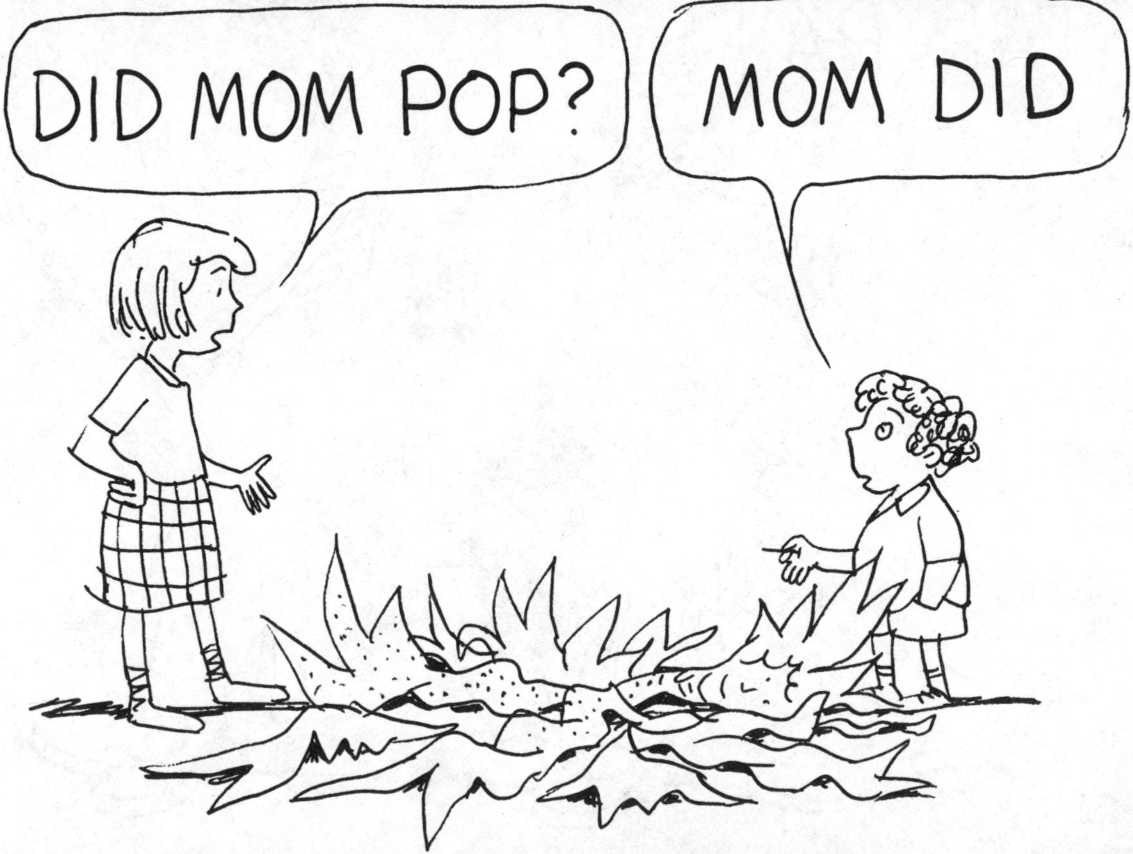
DID MOM POP?
MOM DID

NEIL, AN ALIEN

A CAR, A MAN, A MARACA

DUMP
MUD

EMIL'S NIECE, IN SLIME

ED IS ON NO SIDE

SUB'S KNOB BONKS BUS

ELSIE'S ON A NOSE ISLE

POOH'S HOOP

DAMON,
A NOMÁD

TABOO BAT

OOZY RAT
IN A SANITARY ZOO

Thanks to

Dan Allen, Tom Bassmann, John Baumann,
Russell Busch, Dan Feigelson, Holly McGhee,
Phil Warton, Maria Warton-Bennett and
Stephen Wolf for their contributions.

Racecar Level DAD

KOOK SIS deed

KAYAK Civic Madam

Otto Stats Bob ANNA

reviver DUD